GO TO THE ANT

Sir Ghillean Prance's epic and enduring global career as a botanist, environmental advocate and Christian leader has been an inspiration to a whole generation of conservationists, secular and believing. Any of his writing is worth serious consideration as few bring such a wealth of experience and thought to these vital issues of how life is to continue on God's good earth at a time of such severe crisis.

Peter Harris, Co-founder of A Rocha

GO TO THE ANT

Reflections on biodiversity and the Bible

Ghillean T. Prance

wild goose
publications

www.ionabooks.com

© Ghillean T. Prance
First published 2013 by
Wild Goose Publications,
Fourth Floor, Savoy House,
140 Sauchiehall Street, Glasgow G2 3DH, UK,
the publishing division of the Iona Community.
Scottish Charity No. SC003794.
Limited Company Reg. No. SC096243.

ISBN 978-1-84952-219-9

Cover design © 2013 Wild Goose Publications

The publishers gratefully acknowledge the support of the Drummond Trust,
3 Pitt Terrace, Stirling FK8 2EY in producing this book.

Overseas distribution
Australia: Willow Connection Pty Ltd, Unit 4A, 3–9 Kenneth Road,
Manly Vale, NSW 2093
New Zealand: Pleroma, Higginson Street, Otane 4170, Central Hawkes Bay
Canada: Bayard Distribution, 10 Lower Spadina Ave., Suite 400, Toronto,
Ontario M5V 2Z

Printed by Martins the Printers, Berwick upon Tweed

MIX
Paper from
responsible sources
FSC® C013254

INTRODUCTION

The good leave an inheritance to their children's children ...
Proverbs 13:22

Recently I have gained two grandchildren, and so I think a lot more about the future and what it might hold for them. As I look at what my generation has done to the environment, I get more and more worried about the future. We are nearing a stage of climate change that could be irreversible, and we are losing so many of the plants and animals that help to hold together the world ecosystem – I am ever more concerned about leaving an environment in which future generations can live than in leaving material goods to my grandchildren.

In this book I have tried to express my concern in a series of thoughts based on biblical texts about a wide range of organisms and also on my experience as a tropical botanist who has travelled widely on all continents. It is my hope that this short book of meditations will move Christians to wonder at some of the marvels of nature, and so to treat God's creation with more reverence and respect. Some of the texts I have chosen lead to devotional thoughts and others to interesting details about natural history or environmental concerns. As we shall see, the writers of the Bible were good observers of nature who understood the world around them.

All the main Bible quotations are from the New Revised Standard Version, unless otherwise noted.

Thanks to my wife, Anne, and Eric Holdstock for reading and making helpful comments on an earlier draft of the typescript. I especially thank Neil Paynter for his careful and thorough editing and many helpful suggestions.

Ghillean T. Prance

1

Go to the ant, you lazybones; consider its ways, and be wise.
Proverbs 6:6

The ants are a people without strength, yet they provide their food in the summer.
Proverbs 30:25

Ants are wonderful creatures! They are abundant in the rainforest and play a vital role in the ecology in many ways, such as by dispersing seeds, decomposing vegetation and defending plants against attack from other insects. How often I've sat in the rainforest watching a colony of leafcutter ants laboriously hauling chunks of leaf much larger than themselves along their well-worn trail to their underground colony. The leaves are taken to large chambers where they are used to cultivate the fungus that is the ants' principal food. It is the worker ants from the mediae caste who carry out this first vital task. At the entrance to their burrows are large soldier ants who are the guards. In addition, one can often see tiny 'minor' fighter ants around the foraging trails, who often ride on the backs of the workers to defend them from predators. Underground there is another caste called minims, even smaller than the minors, and their job is to tend the crops by cultivating the fungus and removing unwanted detritus; the minims are the agriculturalists.[1] These ants, and other social insects, are hard workers, and no matter what category an individual belongs to all work together for the common good of the whole colony and their queen.

Unlike the tropical leafcutter ants of the rainforest, the ants of Palestine have to gather enough food in the spring and summer when it is available to prepare an adequate food store for winter. And this led the writer Agur, the author of some of the Book of Proverbs, to comment on their ways. These workers, too, all collaborate for the common good of their community.

The common good is an important principle, and one that is promoted many times in scripture. In the Book of Nehemiah we read that after Nehemiah had called on the people of Jerusalem to rebuild the walls of the city, the Israelites *'committed themselves to the common good'* (Neh 2:18). Today we live in adversarial times where self-interest abounds and people form 'self-interest groups'. The common good is seldom considered, as has been highlighted in the recent financial crisis caused by greed and selfishness. The current environmental crisis is so great and therefore a lot of collaboration will be needed to avoid total disaster. People will have to work together and make sacrifices together if there is to be any serious progress.

Note:

1. Information from The Leafcutter Ants: Civilisation by Instinct, *by Bert Holldobler and Edward O. Wilson, Norton, New York, 2011*

2

Out of the ground the Lord God made to grow every tree that is pleasant to sight and good for food, the tree of life also in the midst of the garden, and the tree of the knowledge of good and evil.

Genesis 2:9

I love this verse because it puts the aesthetic value of trees first and their utility second. If the world were to obey this principle and order of priority then there would not be so much destruction of the forests upon which we depend for so many things. All over the world our first priority has been to use natural resources with little appreciation of their beauty or the environmental services they perform.

I think of the toromiro tree (*Sophora toromiro*) of Easter Island, or Rapa Nui, off the coast of Chile. This was one of the most useful trees to the Polynesian settlers there. It was used for their famous wood carvings, for building and many other things. When the explorer Thor Heyerdahl visited the island, he collected seeds from the one remaining toromiro tree, which died soon afterwards, leaving the species extinct in its native habitat. No wonder the civilisation of Easter Island collapsed and became only a remnant of its former glory, for they had completely deforested the island. Fortunately the seeds of the toromiro that Heyerdahl collected germinated in various botanic gardens in Europe and so the species was not completely lost. Today efforts are being made to reintroduce the toromiro back to Rapa Nui.

This practice of using the very last individual of a useful species was by no means confined to the natives of Easter Island. It is a much more general part of our unsustainable, greedy Western lifestyle, which does not think of the needs of future generations.

Some of the Native American tribes of the woodlands of eastern North America come much closer to taking the advice of this verse from Genesis. When a decision affecting the environment is to be made, they consider what the effect will be on *the seventh unborn generation*. The Western world of today does not even consider what sort of an environment we are leaving for our *grandchildren* to inherit.

Trees are indeed pleasant to sight, and so as we admire these wonders of creation I hope we can be moved to do more to preserve them. This is why I am so happy to be the President of the International Tree Foundation and to be involved with other organisations that are working to conserve trees and other plant species.

3

'Take with you seven pairs of all clean animals, the male and its mate; and a pair of the animals that are not clean, the male and its mate; and seven pairs of the birds of the air also, male and female, to keep their kind alive on the face of all the earth.'

Genesis 7:2–3

Noah was the first conservationist. His mission was to *'keep offspring of all the animals alive on the earth'*. Whether we take this literally or not there is no doubt that in the story of Noah there is a strong message of God's desire to keep alive the species that he created. Reading on, in Genesis chapter nine, where the covenant is set between God and Noah, we note that it is mentioned *six times* that this was a promise not just to Noah and his descendants but to *'every living creature'*. This last phrase must be important or it would not have been repeated so many times in a single chapter. *Every living creature* is important to God and he wants us to know this. How startlingly this contrasts with our attitude today, as our greedy development as modern humans sends over one thousand species to extinction each year, and probably many more we do not even know about. We should be alarmed that it is calculated that the rate of extinction today is at least a thousand times greater than the natural rate.

I think of the Atlantic coastal forests of Brazil. A study that botanist colleagues and I made some years ago showed that 53% of the tree species there are endemic to this forest, that is, they occur nowhere else in the world. Now only just over 6% of the total area of Atlantic forest remains intact. So it is certain that many species of plants and animals have become extinct there. On the other side of South America, botanist Alwyn Gentry collected on the Centinela Ridge in the Pacific coastal forests of Ecuador, and discovered many new undescribed species of plants. He went back a few years later, and to his dismay found that the ridge had been completely deforested. His new species had probably become extinct almost as they were being given their scientific names. These are just two of many examples of what we are doing to living creatures today, going completely against the intention of God's covenant with Noah, which says:

'As for me, I am establishing my covenant with you and your descendants after you, and with every living creature that is with you, the birds, the domestic animals, and every animal of the earth with you, as many as came out of the ark.'

Genesis 9:9–10 (NRSV)

'I will remember my covenant that is between me and you and every living creature of all flesh; and the waters shall never again become a flood to destroy all flesh. When the bow is in the clouds, I will see it and remember the everlasting covenant between God and every living creature of all flesh that is on the earth.'

Genesis 9:15–16 (NRSV)

4

'But ask the animals, and they will teach you; the birds of the air, and they will tell you; ask the plants of the earth, and they will teach you; and the fish of the sea will declare to you. Who among all these does not know that the hand of the Lord has done this?'

Job 12:7–9

These verses cause me to contemplate further on the extinction of the species. Oh, for the wisdom of Job! What are the animals, the birds, the plants and the fish teaching us today? The list of threatened and endangered species kept by the International Union for the Conservation of Nature (IUCN) is now at over twenty thousand, and the list of species that have *become* extinct increases each year. We all know about the dodo of Mauritius, the American passenger pigeon and the huge ratite birds of New Zealand, but many other lesser-known creatures have also become extinct. Miners used to carry canaries into the mines with them to warn them if a poisonous gas was around and the environment was deadly. Some of the greatest extinctions today are amongst frogs and other amphibians, which are particularly sensitive to environmental change: the death of these species is our warning sign today – but we do not seem to be heeding this.

In the 1970s I had the privilege of visiting a student of mine working in the Monteverde Cloud Forest Preserve in Costa Rica. Since she was studying the pollination of a plant by rice rats we were out in the forest at night. It was the mating time of the beautiful golden toad and I was privileged to see them out scrambling among the roots of the trees. But that is not possible any more as this is one of the amphibian species that has become extinct from drier weather with a distinct dry season. This period of drought never used to occur and is due to the amount of rainforest deforestation in the lowlands of Costa Rica. What we do in one place affects other places because the environment has no frontiers and depends on the services provided by rainfall, vegetation and many other factors.

Particularly threatened are organisms that are adapted to life on mountains. As a boy I studied the alpine plants of Ben Lawers in Scotland. Today data from the Royal Botanic Garden, Edinburgh shows that, due to climate change, these plants are migrating gradually upwards. Since the mountains are low, there will soon be no climate suitable for these alpines.

In North America the attractive rabbit relative the pika lives on mountaintop boulder fields. Its thick fur-coat keeps it warm in winter, but it dies quickly when temperatures reach around 80 degrees Fahrenheit (26.6°C). As climate change causes temperature to rise, pikas are confined to their 'sky islands' and can't escape. Already pikas have disappeared from some of their mountain habitats.[1] It seems that it is the plants and animals that are well-adapted to the cold which are the first to suffer from what we are doing to the climate, such as the polar bear.

How the world has depleted fish populations because of greedy over-fishing and the pollution of rivers and streams is well known.

We should be listening to the strong message that we are receiving from the animals, birds, plants and fish. We need these creatures as part of our survival strategy, and have no right to destroy what God has given us to use, but not abuse.

Note:

1. Information about pikas from New Scientist, *5 October 2002*

5

Then their father Israel said to them ...'Take some of the choice fruits of the land in your bags, and carry them down as a present to the man – a little balm and a little honey, gum, resin, pistachio nuts and almonds.'

Genesis 43:11

These fine products were to be given to Joseph in Egypt, who had requested to see Benjamin, his youngest brother. These were all luxury items. The resin was myrrh, which comes from the tree *Commiphora myrrha*, and features in several other places in the Bible; it was of course one of the gifts that the wise men gave to the baby Jesus. There is some uncertainty about the identity of the balm, but it was another special fragrance and was most likely from another species of *Commiphora*. Pistachio nuts (*Pistacia vera*) and almonds (*Prunus dulcis*) were from commonly planted trees in the Middle East, and are more familiar to us. Israel was sending the very best of his harvest as an offering to a high official of Egypt, who he did not know was his long-lost son. God also requires the first fruits of our harvest, and not the leftovers.

Travelling along rivers in remote parts of Amazonia, I have sometimes stopped at a house of a local resident, someone who lives a very basic life. And I have been humbled by their generosity – as they gave me eggs or a big squash or made coffee from the last grounds in their pot. They would have been deeply offended if I had not accepted their gifts, and so it is important to receive graciously, even though you know that you may be depriving them of a good meal. God loves a cheerful giver.

The lesson from these special and well-thought-out gifts of Israel is to give generously of our best, whether it is to friends or to the stranger or to our church or to any other good cause.

6

For six years you shall sow your land and gather in its yield; but the seventh year you shall let it rest and lie fallow, so that the poor of your people may eat; and what they leave the wild animals may eat. You shall do the same with your vineyard, and with your olive orchard.

Exodus 23:10–11

These verses introduce the biblical principle of leaving a fallow period for the land. This is one of many passages in the Old Testament that call for a land ethic. In an age of such great soil erosion it is time to remember about care for the land. Soil is a very precious commodity and is alive with many microorganisms when it is in good shape. It is known that one gram of soil (one fifth of a teaspoon) can contain 100 million bacteria, one million actinomycetes and 100,000 fungi! These microscopic organisms decompose organic residues, synthesise humus and cycle nutrients such as carbon and nitrogen. They are an essential element of healthy soil and so methods of agriculture that encourage the work of microorganisms are vital. In addition, soil contains mites, earthworms, ants, nematodes, spiders and animals such as shrews and moles – soil is truly a living organism!

The care and maintenance of soil is essential for any permanent system of agriculture, yet so much of our agriculture ignores this. Most modern agriculture regards soil as simply a mixture of sand and clay that can be chemically treated with nutrients, fungicides and insecticides with all the natural goodness just eroded away. Modern agriculture has removed much of the carbon that is stored in soil and therefore contributed to climate change. Good organic soil is a rich store of carbon.

I think of the experience of the Aymara peoples of the Altiplano of Bolivia, who have an excellent system of fallow. Each year the owners of the fields meet with the elders and the use of the fields is allocated by the chiefs. Some landowners are told to plant amaranth, others potatoes, others quinoa, and so on until all of their potential crops have a place to grow. But each year a few farmers are instructed to leave their fields unplanted in order for the land to recover. Do those people suffer hunger? No, because they receive of the bounty of their neighbours who planted crops.

Attempts by the Bolivian government some years ago to increase land use and help the national economy forced the Aymara to plant all of their land. Their traditional system of agriculture would have collapsed had it not been for the concerted efforts of missionaries, both Catholic and Protestant, to persuade the government to allow the Aymara to revert to their traditional system of agriculture. Perhaps there is less danger of this happening again while the current President of Bolivia is an Aymara.

Then the Lord said to Moses: Take sweet spices, stacte, and onycha, and galbanum, sweet spices with pure frankincense (an equal part of each), and make an incense blended as by a perfumer, seasoned with salt, pure and holy ...'

Exodus 30:34–35

This recipe, given to Moses for the making of the holy incense, contains some ingredients that would have been expensive even at that time:

Stacte: *Liquidambar orientalis or Styrax officinalis*
Onycha: *Cistus ladaniferus* (rockrose)
Galbanum: *Ferula galbaniflua* (fennel)
Frankincense: *Boswellia papyrifera*

All of these plants require preparation in order to extract their fragrant resins or saps. Stacte is a beautiful shrub that grows on the lower hills of Palestine. Incisions are made in its branches to allow the resin to flow; this is gathered in reeds to harden. Stacte is still used in the incense of the Roman Catholic Church. Onycha is a rockrose with attractive white petals with red blotches at the base. It exudes from its leaves a soft glutinous resin which is highly aromatic. It is described as a medicinal plant by the Greek physician Dioscorides (circa 40-90 AD). Galbanum is a species of fennel which grows from Syria to Iran. The plant contains a milky juice that soon hardens. When burned this has a pleasant pungent odour. Frankincense comes from a tree of Arabia, and is familiar to us as a gift given to the baby Jesus. The bark is cut so that the resin flows out from the inner wood. This hardens and becomes brittle and is burned as an incense. It was no easy task for Moses to assemble this array of plants, and trading must have been necessary to obtain the frankincense.

The recipe was for holy purposes only: *'When you make incense according to this composition, you shall not make it for yourselves; it shall be regarded by you as holy to the Lord'* (Exodus 30:37, NRSV). This was no ordinary incense. God demanded the best from his people. I am reminded of the woman who came to Jesus: *'Mary took a pound of costly perfume made of pure nard, anointed Jesus' feet and wiped them with her hair'* (John 12:3, NRS). Nard (*Nardostachys jatamansi*), or spikenard, is an expensive perfume that comes from a plant native to the Himalayan region and would have been traded to the Bible lands. The disciples argued indignantly that this ointment could have been sold and the money given to the poor. Jesus strongly defended Mary's action and told them that she was anointing his body for burial.

Sometimes we are inclined to give to God our second best, but these two biblical examples remind us again to give of our very best, whether in service or in goods.

But among the winged insects that walk on all fours you may eat those that have jointed legs above their feet, with which to leap on the ground. Of them you may eat: the locust according to its kind, and the bald locust according to its kind, the cricket according to its kind, and the grasshopper according to its kind. But all other winged insects that have four feet are detestable to you.

Leviticus 11:21–23

Insects tend to get a bad press in the Bible, and elsewhere. Here, where permission is given to eat certain ones, the number of legs is incorrect, for insects have *six* not four legs. Have you ever eaten insects? Some of them taste quite good. Part of an explorer's life is eating whatever you are offered from the hospitality of local peoples. People in Mexico seem to heed the advice of this text because one is often served, as a pre-dinner nibble, fried grasshoppers, even in the best restaurants – and they taste delicious. I have eaten termite larvae with the Yanomami Indians, the bodies of leafcutter ant queens with the Jarawara, and the larvae of beetles taken from the rotting wood of recently felled palm trees with many other tribes. The Guaraní people of the rainforests of northern Argentina fell *pindo* palm trees (*Syagrus romanzoffianum*) and after a short time beetles will lay their eggs in the trunks. In a few weeks the juicy larvae develop, and then they are harvested, roasted in leaves and eaten as one of the Guaraní's favourite delicacies. They taste rather like bacon. The Guaraní also eat the larvae of a moth which develops in the dying canes of bamboos. When I was visiting in 2005 one species of bamboo flowered and then died. This created extensive habitat for the moths – and the Guaraní had a real banquet.

Some insects are a useful food supplement for many peoples and so we should not despise this use, which is even encouraged in the Bible. It is probable that insects were an important part of the diet of the children of Israel as they wandered the deserts of Sinai.

Insects are a vital part of the biodiversity of the world. Estimates of how many species there are vary from one million to twenty million, because they are so incompletely studied. Some carry disease or have unpleasant stings, but insects are an essential part of creation. They help with the decomposition of organic matter, pollinate many crops and wildflowers, produce foods such as honey and often help to control pests. About one third of the food that we eat in the UK depends upon bees for pollination, yet bee populations are declining due to what we are doing to the environment and because of the toxic sprays used in modern agriculture.

Let us give thanks for insects and do all we can to protect them.

Now when the people complained in the hearing of the Lord about their misfortunes, the Lord heard it and his anger was kindled ... But the people cried out to Moses; and Moses prayed to the Lord ... and the Israelites also wept again, and said, 'If only we had meat to eat! We remember the fish we used to eat free in Egypt for nothing, the cucumbers, the melons, the leeks, the onions, and the garlic ...'

Numbers 11:1, 2, 4, 5

The desert of the Sinai Peninsula is not a good place for growing vegetables, and if you were living a nomadic existence you would not be stationary enough to cultivate them anyway. This bareness was in marked contrast to the fertile Nile Delta from where the Israelites had come. Even as slaves they were obviously used to growing a cornucopia of crops. And the people were obviously not vegetarians for they also complained about the lack of meat, and fish as well. The Israelites complained to Moses, and we read that God was angry with them for their discontent.

These verses about hungry people remind us of how many starving people there are in the world today. I am sure that it is not their complaints that anger God, but rather the complacency of the well-fed world in addressing world hunger. Fifty million people in the world live in absolute poverty and 15 million children die each year of hunger. It is said that *'for the price of one missile, a school full of hungry children could eat lunch every day for 5 years'*. We live in an unjust world.

Until we have lived up to the Millennium Development Goal of reducing world hunger we cannot sit back. This UN sponsored programme, endorsed by 192 nations and 23 international organisations, has as its first goal *'to eradicate extreme poverty and hunger'*. The targets set include halving the number of people living on less than a dollar a day and the number of people who suffer hunger by 2015. The 2010 UN meeting to review progress of this revealed how far short of these goals we are at present. God's anger must be kindled by the way we continue to allow one quarter of our fellow humans to suffer hunger. We can help by supporting the Christian charities that are doing something about this, such as Tear Fund and World Vision.

May the fact that we have cucumbers, melons, leeks, onions, garlic – and so much else – remind us of those who don't even have the most basic foods.

Benaiah the son of Jehoiada was a valiant man of Kabzeel, a doer of great deeds; he struck down two sons of Ariel of Moab. He also went down and killed a lion in a pit on a day when snow had fallen.

1 Chronicles 11:22

This might seem like a strange verse to include here, but it has special meaning for me. I wonder if you remember the sermon preached at your confirmation. When asked to preach the annual 'Lion sermon'* at St Katherine Cree Church in the City of London, I immediately knew what text I must use. It was the one that Bishop Bird, then Assistant Bishop of Worcester, used at my confirmation in the early 1950s. It was so unusual that it has stuck with me ever since.

Benaiah killed a lion inside a pit on a snowy day. That cannot have been an easy thing to do given the weapons available in 700 BC. The theme of the good bishop's sermon was exactly that: Benaiah did a difficult thing. The bishop developed this theme to inform the young confirmation candidates that the life they were embarking upon as Christians would not be easy and that we would have to work hard to maintain our faith and progress on the pilgrimage of Christian life. This was good advice to me and I have often reflected upon it. Interestingly, I met an old school friend in the 1990s, forty years after that confirmation service. This friend, who is an Anglican priest, reminded me of the text about Benaiah. It had stuck with him too, and had guided him through his life. What a gift to be able to preach a sermon to teenagers that they did not forget; and it was about a 'lion' ...

As I pondered the topic of lions, I wondered: What are the hard-to-defeat lions that we need to kill in today's world?

I will mention just three, and I can't help thinking that they are related:

1. The borrowing beyond our means which contributed to the current financial crisis. This is hardly sustainable living.

2. Climate change, caused mainly by our excess emissions of greenhouse gases. Again showing our greedy unwillingness to reduce our lifestyle, or to invest in the alternative technology needed. In addition, 23% of the increase in greenhouse gases is caused by deforestation. Stopping deforestation would directly cut at least that percentage of carbon dioxide emission.

3. The existence of so much poverty in a prosperous world.

As a biologist who travels around the world, I constantly see evidence of climate change. It is the fact that I see change in so many places, and not just locally, which convinces me of the seriousness of human-caused climate change. Two things suffer the most from climate change: wild animals and plants, and the poor people of the world.

Botanists A.H. and R.S.R. Fitter studied the flowering times of 385 species of British flowering plants. They found that in the decade of the 1990s flowering advanced by 4.5 days compared to the previous four decades. 16% of the species advanced by 15 days in that decade. This is a strong biological signal of climate change. Similar data is coming in from all over the world, showing that climate change is having a severe effect on nature.

There is no doubt that the poor of the world do not have the resources to cope with climate change. They are worst affected, yet they are not the people who caused it.

* This sermon is preached to commemorate 'the wonderful escape' of Sir John Gayer, Lord Mayor of London, in 1647: When shipwrecked on the coast of Africa, Sir John encountered a lion, which prowled around him but, in the end, did not attack. In thanksgiving he bequeathed £200 for the relief of the poor, on the condition that a commemorative sermon be preached annually at St Katherine Cree Church. This tradition continues today.

Who provides for the raven its prey, when its young ones cry to God, and wander about for lack of food?

Job 38:41

He gives to the animals their food, and to the young ravens when they cry.

Psalm 147:9

Consider the ravens: they neither sow nor reap, they have neither store-house nor barn, and yet God feeds them. Of how much more value are you than the birds!

Luke 12:24

Ravens seem to be of special importance to God, as they get several mentions in the Bible. Here it is about the fact that they will not go hungry because of God's provision for them. Ravens are easy to feed because they are omnivorous, eating carrion, insects, food waste, cereal grains, berries, fruit and even small animals. God generously supplies the food for ravens, but what has sinful humankind done to aid fellow human beings who are today suffering from poverty and hunger and crying out for food in an extravagantly rich world?

These statistics from the United Nations Human Development Report (1998) are a rebuke to our current economic system and should cause us to ask ourselves where our priorities lie:

Cost of supplying basic education to all children – US$ 6.0 billion/year
Cost of US spending on cosmetics – US$ 8.0 billion/year

Cost of provision of water and sanitation for all – US$ 9.0 billion/year
Cost of spending on ice cream in Europe – US$ 11.0 billion/year

Cost of provision of basic health for all – US$ 13.0 billion/year
Cost of spending on cat food in the US and Europe – US$ 17.0 billion/year

Cost of elimination of malnutrition through improved agriculture –
US$ 40.0 billion/year
Cost of slimming aids to counter obesity and over-eating in the developed
world – US$ 40.0 billion/year

Throughout the Bible it is made clear that care for the poor is part of responsible Christian behaviour, and indeed many Christians have sacrificed much to help the poor. However, overall we have not got very far when a third of the world population still do not have adequate food and one quarter are facing starvation. About 25,000 people die every day from poverty-related causes and many are children (UN figure). Yet there is enough food in the world to feed everyone. 1.1 billion people live on less than a dollar a day and 2.7 billion on less than two dollars a day (World Bank, 2001). Some progress is being made to address this, as the proportion of the developing world's population living in extreme economic poverty fell from 28% to 21% between 1990 and 2001 (World Bank, 2001). Poverty increases in a recession and so the current world economic situation is likely to affect the poor further. Let us take heed of what the Bible says about the poor:

> *How does God's love abide in anyone who has the world's goods and sees*
> *a brother or sister in need and yet refuses help?*
> I John 3:17, NRSV

Those who oppress the poor insult their Maker, but those who are kind to the needy honour him.

Proverbs 14:31, NRSV

Who sent out the wild donkey free? And who loosed the bonds of the swift donkey, to whom I gave the wilderness for a home, and the salt land for his dwelling place?

Job 39:5–6 (NASB)

We usually think of donkeys as domesticated beasts of burden or as pets giving enjoyable rides to children at the seaside, but this text refers to the wild donkey. It is noted that the salt land is his dwelling place. Donkeys are hardy beasts that can survive in marginal habitats. In some places, where they have been introduced and have reverted to their wild condition, they can be very destructive because of their ability to eat almost any sort of vegetation. This happened on some of the Galapagos Islands and conservationists were faced with the dilemma of what to do with these feral beasts that were destroying the native vegetation.

One of the biggest threats to native plants and animals in most parts of the world, especially on islands, is the introduction of alien species that out-compete native ones. I have spent considerable time working in the Hawaiian islands, where alien species are the greatest threat to native flora and fauna. This varies from feral pigs and goats to introduced gingers that push out the native plants, and passion fruit vines that climb over native trees and smother them.

The water hyacinth (*Eichhornia crassipes*) is a native of the rivers of Amazonia. There it never really gets out of hand as there are native predators that control it, such as the manatee, which eats the whole plant, or insects that attack the flowers and reduce the seed set. But in other parts of the tropics it is one of the worst weeds in lakes and rivers. It was introduced to Florida in 1864 for a horticultural exhibit and ever since has been a bad weed there and in other Gulf States. It has reached Africa and India where it blocks rivers, damaging the livelihood of fishermen and boatmen. This is just one of the many alien plants causing chaos to natural ecosystems around the world.

God rejoices in the animals and plants that he has created, even the water hyacinth, but humankind has messed things up seriously by upsetting the balance of nature in many parts of the world. Organisms have been put together that were never meant to coexist.

The donkey saw the angel of the Lord standing in the road, with a drawn sword in his hand; so the donkey turned off the road, and went into the field; and Balaam struck the donkey, to turn it back onto the road ... The angel of the Lord said to him, 'Why have you struck your donkey these three times? I have come out as an adversary, because your way is perverse before me.'

Numbers 22:23, 32

This strange but fascinating story is of a domesticated rather than a wild donkey, belonging to Balaam. Balaam had set out on a journey, following God's instructions, but God still needed to teach him a lesson in order to strengthen his ability to give the right message to King Balak. An angel confronts Balaam, the angel invisible to him – but not to his donkey. It is easy to imagine the scene when the donkey refused to proceed – because donkeys are notoriously stubborn. Whenever I use them on expeditions, which isn't often, they never want to follow instructions or to walk at the pace you wish them to.

At first, the donkey's behaviour may have seemed normal to Balaam, but when the donkey turned off the road and into a field, Balaam began to get cross with the beast and struck her. The donkey then pressed Balaam's foot against a wall, and so he struck her again. Then, as they proceeded back onto the road, the donkey used another tactic, and lay down under Balaam, who struck her again. It was after this that the donkey spoke, saying: *'What have I done to you that you have struck me these three times?'* It was not until after Balaam threatened to draw his sword and the donkey spoke for a second time to point out how she had faithfully served him that Balaam's eyes were opened, and he saw the angel of God standing in the way. The angel reproved Balaam for striking his donkey. It was only after this dressing-down that Balaam was instructed to proceed on his journey.

The lesson here is not about cruelty to animals, but about God's way of testing. Balaam had a difficult message from God to deliver to Balak, which was contrary to Balak's wishes. God needed to be sure that his messenger was strong enough to resist the temptations of wealth that Balak would offer him. After this experience, no matter how hard Balak tries to work on him, Balaam will stick to God's truth.

God used a donkey and an angel to speak to Balaam. Sometimes before a certain task, we need to go through a difficult period or experience that we may not understand at the time, but which is God's way of taking us forward and preparing us.

He would speak of trees, from the cedar that is in Lebanon even to the hyssop that grows in the wall; he would speak of animals, and birds, and reptiles, and fish.

1 Kings 4:33

This verse shows King Solomon's wide knowledge and grasp of the biodiversity around him. Some of the words of wisdom of Solomon regarding nature are given in the Book of Proverbs, such as his observation on ants which gives title to this book. I sometimes like to speculate about what other observations he brought from nature.

It is generally thought that *'the hyssop that grows in the wall'* refers to the caper plant (*Capparis spinosa*). What might have Solomon said about this? Perhaps something like: 'The caper breaks down the walls of the king's palace, yet it flavours his food.'

The caper is a common plant around the Mediterranean, usually growing on cliff faces. The flower-buds of the caper are gathered and pickled to create the familiar flavour that we often use with fish. Ecclesiastes 12:5 laments the time when the caper becomes ineffective. If the buds are not harvested, the caper has attractive large white flowers with pink stamens, which decorate the walls on which it grows. It is named *spinosa* because there are two sharp, reflexed spines at the base of the leaves which help to defend it from predators, such as goats. The use of the caper as a medicinal plant goes back to classical times: the Greek physician Dioscorides described the use of its roots, shoots and leaves in a treatment for inflammation.

The caper is a versatile and interesting plant and it is a pity that we do not know Solomon's words of wisdom concerning it; it is highly likely that it grew on the walls of his palace.

15

Moreover, the fleet of Hiram, which carried gold from Ophir, brought from Ophir a great quantity of almug wood and precious stones. From the almug wood the king made supports for the house of the Lord, and for the king's house, lyres also and harps for the singers; no such almug wood has come or been seen to this day.

1 Kings 10:11–12

There is much debate about the identification of the almug tree. One possibility is the red sandalwood tree (*Pterocarpus santalinus*), a member of the bean or legume family, which is native to southern India. This would indicate that the wood for the temple and the king's house had travelled a long way. This is a special timber wood which is black outside and a rich, ruby red within. The box tree (*Buxus longifolia*) has also been suggested, and it has also been used for musical instruments. Whatever the almug was, it was brought to the king in great quantities. There was also a huge use of cedar in the building of the temple. The overuse of timber trees is not just a recent phenomenon.

These verses record that the almug was seen this one time and did not appear again. Perhaps the reason that this tree is hard to identify is because it was actually made extinct through overuse: a familiar story today.

The Hawaiian chaff flower (*Achryanthes atollensis*) used to occur on the Kure Atoll, Midway Atoll and other islands of the northwestern Hawaiian Archipelago. This perennial shrub was characteristic of areas of sandy soil near to the coasts of these islands. However, the Hawaiian chaff flower became extinct in 1964, the year when the last wild individual was recorded; the extinction likely due to military operations in the archipelago and to it being swamped by alien introduced species that out-competed it.[1]

May the almug and the Hawaiian chaff flower remind us to protect trees and plants and not send them into extinction.

Note:

1. *Information on the Hawaiian chaff flower given to me by a botanist at a lecture in Hawaii.*

'The ostrich's wings flap wildly, though its pinions lack plumage. For it leaves its eggs to the earth, and lets them be warmed on the ground, forgetting that a foot may crush them, and that a wild animal may trample them. It deals cruelly with its young, as if they were not its own; though its labour should be in vain, yet it has no fear; because God has made it forget wisdom, and given it no share in understanding. When it spreads its plumes aloft, it laughs at the horse and its rider ...'

Job 39:13–18

The poor ostrich comes in for some criticism here, and there is also an element of humour as we read of her rising on high and laughing at the horse and rider.

Fortunately the ostrich and various other large flightless ratite birds, such as the rheas of South America, survive today. The ostrich's careless way of abandoning her eggs and young has not led to the extinction of the species. But other similar large birds have become extinct. There were large ratite birds on the islands of Madagascar, the elephant birds, and on New Zealand, the moas. These great birds are no longer around for us to see today because the early settlers in both places found them easy to catch and good to eat, and so these species rapidly became eradicated once humans reached these islands. It took no longer than a hundred years for the Maori to exterminate the eleven species of moas. So often, humans have carelessly used up the whole of a resource, rather than managing it in a sustainable fashion.

Ostriches have a reputation for burying their head in the sand and ignoring what is going on around them. This reminds me, in two ways, of the behaviour of many in today's world, especially some Christian groups. Climate change is probably the gravest crisis facing humanity, yet many Christians deny its importance, or even existence. There is now indisputable evidence that the climate is changing and that the causes are the accumulation of greenhouse gases in the atmosphere through our use of fossil fuels and our destruction of forests. Another denial also ignores scientific evidence: the denial of evolution as the mechanism of creation. This troubles me as a scientist who studies the evolution of plants and as a Christian. We need to recognise that God has revealed himself in two ways: through creation and through the scriptures. The two revelations need not be considered incompatible, as many Christians who are scientists have discovered. Since there is so much good scientific evidence of the processes of evolution, as a Christian I must conclude that God has used this method in creation. This does not in any way devalue the wonder and marvels of creation.

'Is it at your command that the eagle mounts up and makes his nest on high? It lives on the rock and makes its home in the fastness of the rocky crag. From there it spies the prey; its eyes see it from far away. Its young ones suck up blood; and where the slain are, there it is.'
Job 39:27–30

I like this text because it is one of several in the Bible that acknowledge the predator/prey relationship that exists in nature. Nature or creation is about competition and the quest for food and survival and we should not deny this, or view the natural behaviours of birds and animals as 'cruel'.

Like the eagle, many humans are meat-eaters. God gave Noah authorisation for this when God said: *'Every moving thing that is alive shall be food for you: I give all to you, as I gave the green plants'* (Genesis 9:3, KJB). Fortunately Noah obviously did not then immediately eat all the animals that he had saved on the ark! We have chosen to eat some of these *'all things'* rather than others, but if you look around at the many cultures of the world, a large range of creatures are eaten. I think again of the variety of things I have eaten with the Yanomami Indians in the Amazon (see reflection 8), such as beetle and termite larvae, frogs and queen ants.

Job's observations were correct, for eagles are renowned for their excellent eyesight. They have two foveae, or centres of focus, which allow them to see both forward and to the side at the same time, a great asset for a hunter. Bald eagles are capable of seeing fish in the water from several hundred feet above. This is a remarkable feat, since most fish are counter-shaded, meaning they are darker on top and thus harder to spy from above. For blinking, eagles have an inner eyelid called a nictitating membrane. Every three or four seconds, this membrane slides across the eye from front to back, wiping dirt and dust from the cornea. Because the membrane is translucent, the eagle can see even while the membrane is over the eye. Eagles have colour vision and their eye is almost as large as a human's – however, its sharpness is at least four times greater than that of the sight of a person with perfect vision. The eagle can identify a rabbit moving at almost a mile away. That means that an eagle, flying at an altitude of 1000 feet over open country, can spot prey over an area of almost 3 square miles from a fixed position, so, as Job observes, *'it can spy out its food from afar'*.[1]

Note:

1. *Eagle information from www.baldeagleinfo.com/eagle/eagle2.html. Gathered and written by Hope Rutledge. Used by permission of Hope Rutledge.*

'Look at Behemoth, which I made just as I made you; it eats grass like an ox. Its strength is in its loins, and its power in the muscles of its belly. It makes its tail stiff like a cedar; the sinews of its thighs are knit together. Its bones are tubes of bronze, its limbs like bars of iron ... Under the lotus plants it lies, in the covert of the reeds and in the marsh. The lotus trees cover it for shade; the willows of the wadi surround it. Even if the river is turbulent, it is not frightened; it is confident, though Jordan rushes against its mouth. Can one take it with hooks or pierce its nose with a snare?'

Job 40:15–18, 21–24

There has been much debate about the identification of Behemoth and whether Behemoth refers to a real animal or a mythical creature. Many believe that it refers to the hippopotamus, but the description of his tail *'like a cedar'* argues against this. Some writers think that this refers to its penis, so that there is no problem with the other characteristics listed, such as eating grass and having limbs *'like bars of iron'*. The description of Behemoth covered with lotus leaves is very characteristic of hippos. I have often seen hippos covered with aquatic vegetation as they emerged from underneath the water. Whatever the identification of Behemoth, it is a creature of enormous strength created by God, and of such power that Job could never hope to control it. Behemoth and Leviathan (probably the crocodile, which features in Job 41) are both strong and impressive creatures that are mentioned to put Job in his place in the order of creation.

The Bible is not all about the superiority of humans over nature – an attitude that leads to so much environmental destruction around the world, and one which Christians have often been accused of.

In a much-discussed essay published in the journal *Science* in 1967, the historian Lynn White argued that Judeo-Christian theology was fundamentally exploitative of the natural world. He said that the Bible asserts man's dominion over nature and establishes a trend of anthropocentrism, and that Christianity makes a distinction between man (formed in God's image) and the rest of creation, which has no *'soul'* or *'reason'*, and is thus inferior. He proposed that these beliefs have led to an indifference towards nature that continues to impact in an industrial, *'post-Christian'* world. He concluded that applying more science and technology to the problem won't help – it is humanity's fundamental ideas about nature that must change: we must abandon *'superior, contemptuous'* attitudes that make us *'willing to use it [the earth] for our slightest whim'*. White's essay was not entirely critical of Christianity, however, for he suggested that we adopt St Francis of Assisi's model of the democracy of creation, in which all creatures are respected and equal and humanity's rule over creation is delimited.[1]

Here we have some verses from the Book of Job that show that we are a part of creation and that there are other creatures of equal or even superior rank. Behemoth is a timely reminder and lesson in humility to us.

1. *Information and wording in this paragraph taken from Wikipedia: http://en.wikipedia.org/wiki/Lynn_Townsend_White,_Jr, 'The Historical Roots of Our Ecological Crisis'*

They are like trees planted by streams of water, which yield their fruit in its season, and their leaves do not wither. In all that they do, they prosper. The wicked are not so, but are like chaff that the wind drives away.

Psalm 1:3–4

This verse reminds me of the flooded, or *várzea*, forest of the Amazon. Trees by streams of water is something that one encounters all the time in Amazonia. It is a wonder of creation how so many different species of trees can tolerate having their trunks immersed in water for several months each year as the rivers rise to their crests at the height of the flood season. Amazonian trees have evolved various mechanisms to withstand the floods, such as losing their leaves, or going dormant during the flood, or putting out aerial roots above or near water level. Botanists can detect whether they are in an area that becomes seasonally flooded or on 'terra firma', which is never flooded, by the composition of the forest. Most species are confined to one of these forest types and only a few can grow in both the floodplain and the higher non-flooded forest.

I have often taken tourists out in canoes through the flooded forest. They find it hard to believe that the apparent bushes that we are floating around are in fact the crowns of trees and below there may be a trunk of ten metres or more. There is a lot hidden under the dark black, coffee-coloured water. I am reminded of Paul's words after his famous writing about love: *'For now we see in a mirror, dimly, but then we will see face to face. Now I know in part; then I will know fully, even as I have been fully known'* (1 Corinthians 13:12, NRSV). There is a lot that we do not know in our Christian pilgrimage and we have to accept this on faith. As we travel on our faith journey may we emulate the righteousness of the psalmist rather than the actions of the wicked, that we may not wither.

20

You make springs gush forth in the valleys; they flow between the hills, giving drink to every wild animal; the wild asses quench their thirst. By the streams the birds of the air have their habitation; they sing among the branches.

Psalm 104:10–12

The trees of the Lord are watered abundantly, the cedars of Lebanon that he planted. In them the birds build their nests; the stork has its home in the fir trees.

Psalm 104:16–17

Water is becoming a scarce resource around the world and it is often said that future wars will be fought over water rather than oil. Water is a simple molecule formed from two gases, oxygen and hydrogen, yet it is the whole reason that life on earth is possible. The world has abundant water resources, yet in many places they are being overused. The large underground reservoirs or aquifers are being tapped at far greater than replenishment rates and wells need to be dug increasingly deeper to find water. In some places freshwater streams have become so polluted that fish no longer survive in them. We take water for granted in places where it flows freely from the tap – so pure we can drink it. In 2000, a UN-backed report by the World Commission on Water for the 21st Century stated that half the world's population is living in unsanitary conditions without access to clean water. The report says that three billion people live in squalor and misery without access to proper sanitation – one billion have no access to safe water at all. This is quite a condemnation of those of us in the developed world – that we continue to allow this to happen.

The first text here is about water for wild animals, and they too are suffering today as humans divert streams, and cause unprecedented climate change to which many animals will not be able to adapt. One of the great experiences of life is to be able to visit a waterhole in a dry country such as Namibia and to watch all the wild animals congregate there to drink. Creation was designed with springs and streams *giving water for every beast to drink*. Unfortunately this is no longer the case in many places, due to what we are doing to the environment.

I will never forget being in the Amazon region in 2005, the year of a great drought. Perennial streams dried up and villages that depend on river transport for their livelihood were cut off. The smell of rotting fish in dry lakes and rivers was unbearable. This is what occurs when we disrupt the climate. The 2005 drought in Amazonia was said to be a once-in-a-hundred-years phenomenon, but 2010 brought an even more severe drought to the region, perhaps indicating that a major change in climate is taking place.

The righteous flourish like the palm tree, and grow like a cedar in Lebanon. They are planted in the house of the Lord; they flourish in the courts of our God. In old age they still produce fruit; they are always green and full of sap, showing that the Lord is upright; he is my rock, and there is no unrighteousness in him.

Psalm 92:12–15

He covered the two doors of olivewood with carvings of cherubim, palm trees, and open flowers; he overlaid them with gold, and spread gold on the cherubim and on the palm trees.

1 Kings 6:32

At that time Deborah, a prophetess, wife of Lappidoth, was judging Israel. She used to sit under the palm of Deborah between Ramah and Bethel in the hill country of Ephraim; and the Israelites came up to her for judgement.

Judges 4:4–5

The palm tree that would have been known to the psalmist is of course the date palm (*Phoenix dactylifera*), which is the most prominent tree in the region and provides sustenance for many. It is known as the 'tree of life' to desert people.

Most palm trees are majestic and upright and so it is not surprising that they are likened to the righteous here, and that images of palms were used as decoration and a symbol in Solomon's temple. It was also palm branches that were strewn in front of Jesus as he entered Jerusalem for Passover, and his final moments on earth. The fan of leaves from a palm provides a fine shade and Deborah must have been sheltered and comfortable judging underneath the protection of her palm tree. I have often used fronds of palm to thatch the roofs of our temporary camps in the Amazon forest.

I think of one of my adventures: One time – after spending over two months walking through the rainforest, moving from one jungle airstrip to another – we had used up all our supplies of food, and so were looking forward to the arrival of the plane bringing in new supplies. The plane crash-landed at the airstrip, fortunately without injury to the pilot and others on board. However, because our regular plane was grounded due to an insurance technicality, our pilot had hitched a ride on an Air Force plane, and unfortunately they had decided to bring the people in first, and the supplies on a second flight – and so we were left in the forest with no food and five more people to feed: two pilots and a mapping team of three astronomers, who had never been in the jungle before.

We set to work to fend for ourselves. While the astronomers were sent to fish, I and my field assistant José Ramos searched for edible plants. We came across an old, long-abandoned Indian field with a grove of peach palm (*Bactris gasipaes*). This palm has a very spiny trunk, but we soon cut a stick long enough to reach the large hanging bunches of fruits. When the fruits are boiled they taste rather like chestnut and are rich in vitamins. We returned triumphantly to the camp with our bounty and it was served at dinner, where all enjoyed a lot of peach-palm fruit. The next day they were served at breakfast, lunch and dinner, and by the third day there was a notable reduction in consumption. Nevertheless it was these fruits that were the staple that sustained us for the week until we were rescued by another plane. The peach palm was indeed the tree of life to our stranded expedition.

I was once asked in a radio interview: 'If you were stranded on a desert island, which family of plants would you want to be growing there?' I quickly responded the *Arecaceae*, or the palm family. The palm provides food, medicines, thatching, needles and many other resources, and so it is not surprising that it is given prominence in the Bible.

22

The high mountains are for the wild goats; the rocks are a refuge for the coneys.

Psalm 104:18

To humans the high mountains of the desert regions of the East are a hostile environment in which it is difficult to survive. One of the wonders of creation is that there are plants and animals adapted to the harshest of ecosystems. Goats are notorious for their ability to eat almost anything and this is part of their strategy for survival in the mountains. Another quality is their ability to climb up to the most unlikely places to graze. I have watched goatherds leading their flocks along the most hazardous cliffs in Turkey and Morocco and have been amazed that neither the goats nor the herders fall. When I was on a plant-collecting expedition in Turkey in 1960 we found that one of the problems for us was that goats had eaten most of the vegetation. These animals are anathema to the botanist and seemed to be ubiquitous in many of the areas where we wanted to collect. To get good plant specimens we had to go where the goats could not. This was not easy because there are few places that a goat cannot reach. If we had not been equipped with climbing ropes our plant collections would have been much less useful.

Goats are destroying the vegetation in many other places in the world where I have worked. This is very true in the semi-desert region of northeast Brazil. Royal Botanic Gardens, Kew is involved in a project in that region called 'Plants of the Northeast'. Its goal is to encourage the use of local plants by local people. One of the programmes of 'Plants of the Northeast' involves goats. Traditionally local people have allowed their goats to wander everywhere. The goat fodder programme involves using a series of corrals planted with fast-growing, nitrogen-fixing legume trees. The goats are allowed to graze in one of four corrals while the other enclosures are recovering from grazing. By rotation through these enclosures the goats are better fed and do not destroy the native vegetation. The goat owners are pleased with the results of the programme as the yields of both milk and meat are higher from these goats than from the free-roaming animals.

Wild goats live in extreme environments and are an integral part of creation. Domesticated goats can be most destructive, or they can be responsibly managed and be an important source of milk and meat. They teach us to consider how we use the different elements of nature and to manage them in ways that do not destroy the environment.

The coneys (rock badgers) that feature in this verse are discussed in reflection 25.

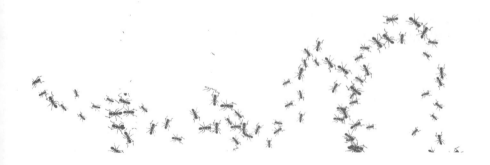

23

You make darkness, and it is night, when all the animals of the forest come creeping out. The young lions roar for their prey, seeking their food from God. When the sun rises they withdraw and lie down in their dens.

Psalm 104: 20–22

Animal life is divided into two major cohorts, those that are diurnal, or active during the day, and those that are nocturnal and only emerge at night when it is dark. The average person knows much less about the second group because we do not regularly go out at night, or when we do, we use illumination to find our way around and this scares the creatures of the night. Owls are probably the best-known nocturnal creatures as they are often heard, and are featured in many children's stories.

This division between night and day is part of nature's economy and the best use of its resources, and it is good to see this recognised by the psalmist, who had observed the habits of lions. Just recently, in Namibia, I was taken by a guide into the midst of a pride of sleeping lions in the middle of the day. The lions did not seem to mind the presence of our open Land Rover – within only two metres from some of them. However, at night we were not allowed to walk back to our cabin without an escort for fear that these same lions might attack us. The tourist camp was taking advantage of their knowledge of the behaviour of these lions.

I have spent many nights in the Amazon rainforest making biological observations – and indeed, as the text above says, the beasts of the forest *do* prowl about. One encounters many more animals on a nocturnal foray into the forest. It is at night that I have seen jaguars, and many more snakes and tarantulas. The optics of nocturnal animals are a wonder of nature. The large eyes of various lemurs and opossums enable them to see in the dark.

Not all night animals are prowling about, some are flying, such as nightjars and bats. Bats are not popular with many people, who have false fears of them, but they are a vital part of the ecosystem. They visit flowers to gather nectar and thereby pollinate them, and they eat fruit and thereby disperse the seeds of many plants.

I have studied the *pequiá* tree (*Caryocar villosum*) of the Amazon forest. This is one of the largest trees, and at flowering time the inflorescences emerge above the crowns of the trees. At dusk an observer begins to observe bats arriving at the flowers and sticking their noses into the centres to obtain the nectar. In the process, they become well-dusted with pollen. Each inflorescence tends to have only one or two open flowers on any night and so a single tree does not satisfy the needs of the bats, and so they fly on to other trees for more nectar and thereby cause pollination. Other bat-pollinated trees, such as the species of the legume genus *Parkia*, have flowers that dangle down below the canopy of the tree on long stalks. The flowers of bat-pollinated species must be readily available and not inside the branches because one of the adaptations of bats to their nocturnal life is navigation by echolocation rather than by sight. This would not work well inside a mass of branches, but easily leads them to flowers that rise up above the canopy or hang down beneath it.

The *sapucaia* nut, or monkey pot (*Lecythis ollaria*), a relative of the Brazil nut, produces its fruit in large urns. The lid falls off this large woody fruit when it is mature and the rest of the fruit remains hanging on the tree.

Once the lid drops off, bats arrive at night and take out the seeds which are borne on a thick, fleshy, foul-smelling stalk. They fly away and eat the stalk but discard the seeds, thus dispersing them around the forest.

Whether lions or bats or people, all creatures rely on God who gives us our daily bread.

24

Three things are too wonderful for me; four I do not understand:
the way of an eagle in the sky,
the way of a snake on a rock,
the way of a ship on the high seas,
and the way of a man with a girl.

Proverbs 30:18–19

Two of the things that the wise oracle Agur did not understand were from wild nature. It is indeed a wonderful sight to watch an eagle soaring. The slightest movement in the arrangement of its feathers causes it to change direction. It is an expert in using the thermals, thereby using little energy as it covers great ground. We know a lot more about the flight of birds than they did in Agur's day.

One of the world's largest eagles lives in the Amazon: the majestic harpy eagle, which I have only seen on three occasions as it has become scarce through being hunted and because many of the large trees upon which it depends for nesting have been destroyed. It usually uses the kapok tree (*Ceiba pentandra*), which has an umbrella-like crown and large, spreading branches; the harpy builds its nest in the crotches of these branches. I have once had the privilege of seeing a nest with two harpy chicks in it in the rainforest of Amazonian Ecuador. The harpy hunts monkeys and sloths as its main source of food.

Agur is probably wondering why snakes come out in the heat of the day and lie on rocks to warm themselves. This is part of the strategy of cold-blooded animals, or poikilotherms, which need to use the sun directly because they do not have the warm-blooded system that keeps our body temperature constant.

Science has explained many of the things that would have puzzled Agur and Solomon and caused them to wonder at creation. But having the knowledge of how something in nature works should not diminish our essential wonder – and our wonder at how it interacts with other organisms. The control of body temperature is such a complicated system, yet most of the time we humans keep close to the normal temperature: how wonderful that whether you are an Inuit in the frozen Arctic or an Yanomami Indian in the heat of the Amazon rainforest your body temperature is about 37°C. As I learn more about the intricate workings of nature, it strengthens, rather than diminishes, my faith in the creator God.

25

The badgers are a people without power, yet they make their homes in the rocks; the locusts have no king, yet all of them march in rank; the lizard can be grasped in the hand, yet it is found in kings' palaces.

Proverbs 30:26–28

I like these verses, which are also said to be the words of Agur the oracle. As one would expect from an oracle, whose job included observing the natural world around him and drawing lessons from it, Agur obviously took these things seriously. Today we are so far removed from nature. This passage is a reminder that even in the midst of the many distractions and diversions of modern city-life, we can look and learn from the remnants of nature that are still around us.

The words of this text are from a wise person who is humbled by the marvels of nature. That locusts are admired is interesting because when they do swarm they are agents of destruction. Yet the writer can see beyond this and admire their orderliness and apply lessons from it. As locusts crawl along the ground they walk in a specific direction: we do not always need a leader. It is good when people volunteer to help without being told. They just see the need and pitch in.

The word translated as rock badger in most versions of the Bible might actually refer to Arabian mice. Arabian mice are weak, shy creatures which make their homes in the rocks so that they are well-guarded and protected. Could this not remind us of the Rock in which we can secure our lives, Jesus the Christ? The lesson from rock badgers to us is to 'hide' (Colossians 3:3) in Christ, who is our refuge and strength.

The lizard probably refers to the gecko. How often I've sat in a house in the tropics and been fascinated watching the antics of these curious creatures running up and down the walls and across ceilings. In the tropics one can't avoid having these companions in one's house – which is in fact most useful because of all the insects that they eat – and here we are informed that they even enter into kings' palaces.

We may not be fond of locusts, mice and creeping lizards, but they all have useful functions within nature and are part of God's wonderful creation.

I am a rose of Sharon, a lily of the valleys. As a lily among brambles, so is my love among maidens.

Song of Solomon 2:1–2

The rose of Sharon is often referred to in church songs, but in fact it is quite uncertain what species of plant this actually is. It is unlikely to be a rose in the plant genus *Rosa*. In modern horticulture, various species of hypericum, St John's wort and hibiscus are called rose of Sharon, but these are certainly not the plant referred to in the Song of Solomon. The most widely agreed interpretation of this biblical plant (*chabazeleth* in Hebrew) is *Pancratium maritimum*, or the sea daffodil, which blooms in late summer and has elegant white flowers. This species also features on a Minoan bronze dating from 1560 BC. Other candidates include species of tulips, crocuses and gladioli, all of which grew abundantly on the plains of Sharon in Palestine. One species of tulip is named *Tulipa sharonensis*, and this could well be this biblical plant.

Although not a biblical image, Jesus is often referred to as the rose of Sharon for his perfectness and purity. In the Song of Solomon, the rose of Sharon is used to describe the beauty of a young woman and love for her. Jews interpret this to symbolise the relationship between God and Israel. Christians take it to represent the relationship between Jesus Christ and his Church. The New Testament refers to Jesus as the Bridegroom and the Church as his Bride, again using love imagery to describe the intimate personal relationship that God wants us to establish with Jesus.

Your channel is an orchard of pomegranates with all choicest fruits, henna with nard, nard and saffron, calamus and cinnamon, with all the trees of frankincense, myrrh and aloes, with all chief spices ...

Song of Solomon 4:13–14

This passage is one of the most biodiverse in the Bible – no less than nine different plants are used in this extravagant praise of the bride in the Song of Solomon.

These plants have varying uses, but are all known for their pleasing aromas. Some of their uses are listed at the end of this reading.

This Bible passage indicates that King Solomon had an extensive knowledge of plants. Some of these, such as the pomegranate, are native to the Bible lands, but the verses show the extent of the movement of plant materials across the globe by that time: cinnamon comes from the Spice Islands of Indonesia and myrrh is from North Africa.

Aromatherapy is a modern concept, but it has been used, if not termed as such, since ancient times. How agreeable and relaxing it feels to be sitting in a steaming hot bath with the scent of some plant extract wafting around you. This selection of sensuous plants reminds us of ways to relax using our olfactory and gustatory senses when we are experiencing times of stress and trouble.

Pomegranate, *Punica granatum* – edible fruit

Henna, *Lawsonia inermis* – cosmetic and ornamental body paint

Nard, *Nardostachys jatamansi* – perfumed ointment

Saffron, *Crocus sativus* – flavouring for food, ornamental flower

Calamus, *Acorus calamus* – used in cosmetics and perfumes

Cinnamon, *Cinnamomum verum* – flavouring for food and drinks

Frankincense, *Boswellia papyrifera* – an expensive incense from a resin

Myrrh, *Commiphora myrrha* – medicine, opiate, perfume

Aloe, *Aquilaria malaccensis* – an expensive fragrance made from the wood

28

The ox knows its owner, and the donkey its master's crib; but Israel does not know, my people do not understand.

Isaiah 1:3

I remember when I was a boy riding to places where I wanted to collect plants, that the pony usually went lethargically on the outward journey, needing much coaxing to venture further from home. But as soon as I turned it slightly in a homeward direction, it began to trot enthusiastically, and I had no need to encourage it along that way.

Isaiah obviously had a similar sort of experience with his donkey or had observed this behaviour in other people's beasts of burden. He also observes how an ox knows its owner in contrast to a stranger. A cattle farmer usually has a close relationship with each member of his herd. Any dog owner knows how a dog greets the homecoming of its master enthusiastically with much tail-wagging. The prophet Isaiah contrasts his observations of animal behaviour with the ungodly behaviour of Israel. The verse following the above text begins *'Alas, oh sinful nation'*, words that are apposite today.

Isaiah is lamenting the fact that Israel does not recognise the Lord and that the nation is lost and does not know the way home. The church of today is often lost and in need of finding the way back to the basics of Christian teaching and living. This verse is a pertinent reminder to us to keep God in the forefront and to find our eventual way home to heaven through our faith in Christ, our actions and our prayer life.

But the hawk and the hedgehog shall possess it; the owl and the raven shall live in it; He shall stretch the line of confusion over it, and the plummet of chaos ... Thorns shall grow over its strongholds, nettles and thistles in its fortresses. It shall be a haunt of jackals, an abode for ostriches. Wildcats shall meet with hyenas, goat-demons shall call to each other; there too Lilith shall repose, and find a place to rest. There shall the owl nest and lay and hatch and brood in its shadow; there too the buzzards shall gather, each one with its mate.

Isaiah 34: 11,13–15

Isaiah's prophecy of the end of Edom is also a lesson in natural history. It shows the prophet's extensive knowledge of the environment around him. It is also an excellent description of the way in which nature takes over when a human-made habitat is abandoned or destroyed. Creation has a wonderful regenerative power and any vacant space is soon filled again by plants and animals.

Evidently the hedgehog – one of my favourite animals – was a symbol of desolation to Isaiah, as he also mentions them in his prophecy to Babylon: *'I will also make it a possession of the hedgehog ... and I will sweep it with the broom of destruction'* (Isaiah 14:23, NRSV). This reminds me of the desolation that I have witnessed in many places where the rainforest has been cut down. The wonderfully diverse forest is replaced by a short-term form of agriculture and one sees the half-burnt skeletons of the once-majestic trees in the midst of a pasture or field of some crop. These trees stand like tombstones announcing the death of the rainforest. Such fields are later abandoned because of the poor soil, and the desolation is worse.

However, after a few years, the vegetation begins to return again as secondary coloniser species are seeded over the area, and just as Isaiah noticed, some animals also begin to return with the succession of regeneration. It takes a long time for the original forest to return, but the regenerative resilience of nature or creation is soon apparent. This can bring hope to those scientists who are working on the restoration of destroyed environments. It is good to note that restoration ecology is a growing discipline today.

The wilderness and the dry land shall be glad, the desert shall rejoice and blossom; like the crocus it shall blossom abundantly, and rejoice with joy and singing. The glory of Lebanon shall be given to it, the majesty of Carmel and Sharon. They shall see the glory of the Lord, the majesty of our God.

Isaiah 35:1–2

Isaiah uses the crocus here as a sign of hope. Crocus blossoms are one of the first to emerge in the late winter or early spring. They are a sign of rebirth and renovation and many gardeners wait for them eagerly – after a harsh winter how glad we all are to see this sign that spring will soon be here.

I think of the wonderful blue-and-white carpet of crocuses that each spring decorates the lawn of the Royal Botanic Gardens at Kew. These were planted in 1987 to bring joy to the people of London, who flock to see this sign of new life and the beginning of a new season.

The crocus lawn at Kew blossoms profusely as it has been densely planted. The prophet must have seen a field of wild crocuses somewhere in his travels as abundant as the one at Kew. In the wild today, though, this is a sight that is all too rare, due to our destruction of the environment.

As I read these verses of new hope I think about the need for the restoration of natural habitats. But from the image of the crocus I also think of the personal rebirth that is available to us through the sacrifice of Jesus on the cross and the Resurrection. All we need to do is to ask Christ to come into our life and then we too will experience the glory of the risen Lord.

He will feed his flock like a shepherd; he will gather the lambs in his arms, and carry them in his bosom, and gently lead the mother sheep.
Isaiah 40:11

The lamb means so much symbolically to Christians, who follow the teaching of the Good Shepherd. In our culture and in the Bible lands these creatures are familiar, and so it is relevant to use them in metaphors and parables to illustrate points.

I had never really thought much about this, until I was working in the Amazon rainforest using a missionary, Fritz Herter, as a translator to help communicate with the Yanomami Indians, who were working for us. One evening Fritz and I were discussing the work he was doing translating the Gospel of John into Yanomami. The Yanomami are an isolated people who have obviously never even seen a sheep. 'So how do you cope with that?' Fritz asked me. Jesus said, in one of the many references to sheep in John's Gospel: *'I am the good shepherd. I know my own and my own know me'* (John 10:14, NRSV). The Yanomami, and many other indigenous tribal people, do not even domesticate similar animals; and the only pets the Yanomami have are hunting dogs, which they tend to ill-treat, so it would not do to use dogs as an example in a biblical translation. What Fritz eventually did was to use a deer as an example, because one of the village children had raised a young deer to adulthood and it remained a pet, as the youngster was so attached to it.

One of my childhood memories is of Mr Laight, a neighbour in the

Cotswolds who was an elderly retired shepherd. He was a most friendly and kind person and he used to fascinate me with his tales of how he had taken such good care of his sheep. He even still had a shepherd's crook leaning up against the porch of his house. Most of his stories were about experiences with one individual animal, demonstrating the truth in the biblical metaphor of the shepherd's love for one lost sheep. We have a loving God who cares for each one of us.

32

I will put in the wilderness the cedar, the acacia, the myrtle, and the olive; I will set in the desert the cypress, the plane and the pine together, so that all may see and know, all may consider and understand, that the hand of the Lord has done this; the Holy One of Israel has created it.

Isaiah 41:19–20

As someone who has spent his life studying trees, this is one of my favourite texts in the Bible. The prophet sees that the purpose of the trees of the wilderness and the desert is to reveal the Creator. His desire is that we may gain understanding from these common and useful trees of the Bible lands.

I think of the first time I entered the rainforest, in Suriname in 1963. The experience was overwhelming – to see the diversity and the size of the trees. Many had buttressed roots at their base, like the buttresses built on to great cathedrals – and I and many others have likened their first time in a rainforest to the experience of entering a cathedral. It has the same awe-inspiring effect, confirming the magnificence of creation and the bounty that has been made available to us by God.

Another place where the trees spoke to me and where this biblical text rang true was on my very first botanical expedition, in Turkey in 1960. We were walking up the Ak Daglari, or the White Mountains, in the southwest of the country through magnificent scenery. Our trail took us through the zone of cedar trees. These are completely different from those planted in an English parkland. In a parkland, cedar trees are regularly spaced out with grassland in between. In a cedar forest they are dense, with just enough space for each tree to spread its branches.

However, the small remaining wild cedar forest that I walked through in awe in Turkey is but a remnant of the former distribution of this great species. Throughout its range the cedar has been felled and put to use. We read about the use of cedarwood in other texts of the Bible, and so the destruction of the cedar forests began centuries ago. We read of Solomon that: *'He built the house and finished it; he roofed the house with beams and planks of cedar'* (I Kings 6:9, NRSV); and *'he lined the walls of the house on the inside with boards of cedar; from the floor of the house to the rafters of the ceiling, he covered them on the inside with wood'* (1 Kings 6:15, NRSV).

Isaiah draws attention to these seven species of trees to remind us that the Holy One of Israel has created them.

33

For you shall go out in joy, and be led back in peace; the mountains and the hills before you shall burst into song, and all the trees of the field shall clap their hands.

Isaiah 55:12

Then shall all the trees of the forest sing for joy.

Psalm 96:12b

Have you ever been among trees in a storm? To be in the rainforest when a sudden storm brews up is both an exciting and a frightening experience. The branches wave about frantically and sometimes rub together making groaning sounds. The structure of the branches is such that they can withstand a lot of waving in the wind. At other times, a branch breaks suddenly off – and that is when you have to be careful where you're standing! But reading this verse from Isaiah, I began to think of the waving branches of the trees clashing together more as a sign of joy. However, I ask, are the trees clapping their hands with joy today as they see their numbers being reduced and their species becoming extinct?

The trees of the English forests were not singing for joy in 2011 when there were plans being made to sell off some of the forests of England into private hands and thereby condemn them to possible destruction. Fortunately the consolidated action of many citizens who signed petitions and wrote to their Members of Parliament reversed the decision and the trees could continue to sing for joy.

Most of the trees in tropical rainforests have leaves with pointed apices, which are termed 'drip tips'. The leaves are designed so that the water runs off them easily and they are not damaged by the weight of it. Often after a storm in the forest one hears the constant dripping from the leaves for hours after it has stopped raining. The drip tip is a useful adaptation of the trees, but sometimes, as I listen to this essential activity, I feel that they are shedding tears for their fellow trees and over what we are doing to them. I also think of the tears shed by the gardeners at the Royal Botanic Gardens, Kew when they witnessed the devastation to the trees they had cared for by the hurricane of October 1987.

This verse tells us about much more than the sounds of rustling leaves in a storm. It shows us the real purpose of creation: to praise God. It is not just humans who were made to worship God – but the whole of creation that joins in this act of bringing pleasure to the Creator. Let us preserve the forests and the trees so that they may continue to clap their hands in praise of God.

34

A multitude of camels shall cover you, the young camels of Midian and Ephah; all those from Sheba shall come. They shall bring gold and frankincense, and shall proclaim the praise of the Lord.

Isaiah 60:6

Camels get several mentions in the Bible, and this is one of the most interesting. It is generally considered a prophecy of the visitation of the wise men to the infant Jesus. Matthew 2:11 adds their third gift, myrrh. Matthew does not mention the type of transport used by the magi, but it is highly likely that they used camels, the main method of long-distance travel in the region at that time.

The camel is a superb example of an animal adapted to the extreme environment in which it lives. Camels are able to withstand changes in body temperature and water content that would kill most other animals. Their body temperature ranges from 34 degrees Celsius at night to 41 degrees during the day, only above which they begin to sweat. A common misconception is that camels store water in their humps; the humps are a reservoir of fatty tissue. This tissue can be metabolised as a source of energy and yields more than a gram of water for each gram of converted fat. Camels can withstand 20-25% loss of weight from sweating and their blood still remains hydrated: most mammals would die at 15% dehydration. Their ability to endure long periods without water is due to several physiological adaptations. Unlike other mammals their red blood cells are oval in shape, which assists the cells to flow even in a dehydrated state. These oval cells are more stable and can withstand high osmotic pressure without rupturing when a camel drinks a large amount of water – often 22 to 23 gallons. This is the only mammal with oval blood cells, while they do occur in some reptiles, birds and fish. Camels have special adaptations in their nostrils that trap much of the water vapour in their breath and return it to the body. The kidneys and intestines of camels are efficient at retaining water, making their urine a thick syrup; their faeces is so dry that it can be used as a fuel for fires. The thick coat of a camel reflects sunlight and insulates it from the desert sun – John the Baptist would have been warm and well-protected in his garment of camel fur (Matthew 3:4) – and a camel's long legs help it by keeping it away from the hot ground. A camel's long eyelashes and ear hairs, as well as sealable nostrils, form barriers against the sand of sandstorms.[1]

These wonderful animals have been domesticated since early times and have helped people to survive in the desert, being a source of milk and meat as well as a means of transport.

Camels remind us of the gifts that we bring to Jesus and of the churches and Christian causes that we support with our donations and tithes.

Note:

1. Camel information and wording taken from www.worldanimalfoundation.net/home.html. Used with permission. Originally taken from various sources, including Wikipedia: http://en.wikipedia.org/wiki/Camel, and edited

35

Even the stork in the heavens knows its times; and the turtledove, swallow, and crane observe the time of their coming; but my people do not know the ordinance of the Lord.

Jeremiah 8:7

There is an appointed time for everything. And there is a time for every event under heaven.

Ecclesiastes 3:1 (NASB)

The scientific literature today contains a lot about the science of phenology: the study of the timing of various events in nature, such as when trees first develop their leaves in spring, flowers open and migratory birds arrive. Early in my career any studies of phenology were simply straightforward observations of these regular events, but today most papers are about the irregularities that are now occurring. Flowers are opening earlier in spring and migratory birds arriving at different times. Botanist Nigel Hepper made observations for many years of the first opening of flowers of some three hundred species at the Royal Botanic Gardens, Kew. He found that on average flowers are opening eight days earlier than they were thirty years ago. This is just one of many phenological studies around the world that show that things are altering because of climate change.

Even isolated peoples are observing changes in the nature around them. In recent years I have spent a lot of time with the Guaraní people in the rainforests of northern Argentina, carrying out studies of the plants they use. We have used many Guaraní informants to research this. The plant that we considered the second most useful in our quantification of uses was one that they call *guembe*. It is a Philodendron (*P. bipinnatifidum*), or elephant's ear plant, which grows high up on the branches and in the crotches of rainforest trees. It provides an edible fruit, medicines and a basketry fibre.

On one expedition I was out in the field with one of our informants, Elvio, when *guembe* was in flower. It was then that I was told of another use that I wasn't aware of. I was informed that when *guembe* flowered it was a signal that it was time to plant corn and other crops, as there would be no further frosts. Then Elvio made the observation that this no longer held true and *guembe* had deceived them in recent years. While we were in the field discussing this, a pair of beautiful swallow-tailed kites flew over on their southern migration. Elvio said that this bird was also a signal that it was time to plant, but that it too was no longer a reliable indicator.

Phenology is recording changes to plants and animals all over the world – from our backyard flower gardens to the rainforests of Argentina. Humankind is drastically altering God's *appointed time for everything*. We ignore these portents at our peril.

36

The thought of my affliction and my homelessness is wormwood and gall! My soul continually thinks of it and is bowed down within me. But this I call to mind, therefore I have hope: The steadfast love of the Lord never ceases, his mercies never come to an end; they are new every morning; great is your faithfulness.

Lamentations 3:19–23

Wormwood and gall are symbols of bitterness in the Bible. Wormwood is a species of *Artemisia*, a member of the daisy family; two species are common in the Bible lands, *A. herba-alba* and *A. judaica*. They are well-known for their bitter taste, and some Arabs still drink an infusion made from their leaves. The identification of gall is less certain. On the cross, Christ was offered wine *'mingled with gall'*. When he tasted it he refused to drink it. St Mark refers to this offering as *'mixed with myrrh'*, which is also a bitter substance, obtained from the resin of the tree *Commiphora myrrha*.

Wormwood and myrrh may be bitter, but both have their good side, as they are important medicines. The best treatment for malaria these days is artemisine, which comes from a species of wormwood. For many years quinine, from the Andes, which also flavours tonic water, was the most important cure. Many of the plants with bitter bark or leaves that I have collected in Amazon rainforests have also been indicated as remedies for fevers and malaria. Many people have used a tincture of myrrh to deaden the throb of toothache – so there is a lot more than bitterness in both of these biblical plants.

The writer of Lamentations is bemoaning his affliction and homelessness. But the same writer speaks of *'the steadfastness of the Lord that never ceases and whose mercies are new every morning'*. The capacity to look beyond the tragedies and sorrows of life and to turn to the Lord is something we should remind ourselves of on a daily basis. This verse is followed by the often quoted and sung words *'Great is your faithfulness'*. It was these words that encouraged and inspired Thomas Obadiah Chisholm (1866-1960), who had suffered much incapacitating illness as a young man. After finding Christ, at the age of 27, he wrote a poem based on Lamentations 3:22–23, which he sent to his friend William Runyan. Runyan found Chisholm's poem so moving that he set it to music. The hymn 'Great Is Thy Faithfulness' was little known until the Moody Bible Institute took it up as a favourite and George Beverly Shea began to sing it at Billy Graham crusades.[1]

Note:

1. *Information and wording on Thomas Obadiah Chisholm and the writing and history of 'Great Is Thy Faithfulness' by Connie Ruth Christiansen, from www.sharefaith.com. Used by permission of Connie Ruth Christiansen*

37

And you, take wheat and barley, beans and lentils, millet and spelt; put
them into one vessel and make bread for yourself. During the number of
days that you lie on your side, three hundred ninety days, you shall eat it.
Ezekiel 4:9

The bread that Ezekiel was commanded to make was good and nutritious, and so he would have been able to survive on it for the three hundred and ninety days, provided he also had enough water to drink. The mixture of cereals and two sorts of beans would have been a good balance of carbohydrates and proteins. Rice and beans, a carbohydrate- and protein-rich diet, is today the staple food of many in Latin America. Spelt is the grain of a more primitive type of wheat and is less used today, though it is sometimes still favoured as it contains less gluten than the hybrid wheat that we normally use to make bread. Each of the cereals (wheat, barley, millet and spelt) contain some differences in micro-nutrients and even types of carbohydrates and so would have given the prophet a good variety of dietary requirements. The beans and lentils would have added not only protein but a lot more nutrition that the cereals do not contain.

This verse reminds us of the many people in the world who do not even have the basic ingredients of this simple recipe available for their nutrition. Today, while the developed world eats excessively and suffers from obesity, 50% of the world's population are undernourished. We should be supporting Christian organisations that are trying to address this problem: Tear Fund, Send a Cow, World Vision and many others.

So the Lord God appointed a bush, and made it come up over Jonah, to give shade over his head to save him from his discomfort; so Jonah was very happy about the bush. But when dawn came up the next day, God appointed a worm that attacked the bush, so that it withered. When the sun rose, God prepared a sultry east wind, and the sun beat down on the head of Jonah so that he was faint and asked that he might die. He said, 'It is better for me to die than to live.'

Jonah 4:6–8

Jonah was running away from God, and the main lesson to be taken from the Book of Jonah is that you can't escape God: for God is everywhere.

No place in the Bible speaks more definitely of God's control of nature: God appointed a great wind, a great fish (or whale), a bush (or vine), a worm (or caterpillar). The whale and the bush were both appointed to rescue Jonah from his troubles. Jonah did not deserve either of these interventions, but this is our loving and compassionate God who seeks out the lost and rescues them rather than letting them drown in their sin. If you are trying to flee God, remember his patience with Jonah, his errant servant.

Jonah was very happy with the vine, which provided shade from the scorching heat of the region, but his attitude was still not right; and so God intervened again with the worm, which caused the vine to wither. Jonah had a false security, trusting in the vine rather than in God. Sometimes a blessing in life is followed by something that is hard to understand, until one turns back to God. The result of Jonah's reluctant message to Nineveh is that both the people and the cattle are spared.

In the Book of Jonah we see God's care for creation: *'And should I not be concerned about Nineveh, that great city, in which there are more than a hundred and twenty thousand persons who do not know their right hand from their left,* and also *many animals?'* (Jonah 4:11, NRSV).

These verses from Jonah should inspire us to take greater care of God's creatures and biodiversity.

Even the sparrow finds a home, and the swallow a nest for herself, where she may lay her young, at your altars, O Lord of hosts, my King and my God.

Psalm 84:3

The common house sparrow must have been an abundant bird in the Bible lands as it gets mentions in both the Old and the New Testament. It seems that sparrows nested in the temples of old. Today they still find their homes in church buildings, along with jackdaws, which are so common in our church towers. Many churches also harbour bats, which are protected animals. Churches and churchyards are some of the most important areas for the conservation of our flora and fauna in the United Kingdom. The way in which they are managed can make all the difference to wildlife and can create sanctuaries for rare plants and animals. For example, not mowing the grass until late in the year allows many butterfly species to prosper. The Reverend Nigel Cooper wrote an excellent book about the role of churchyards in conservation: *Wildlife in Church and Churchyard: Plants, Animals and their Management* (Church House Publishing, 2001).

When I was a boy, sparrows were very common birds around houses and farms and were one of the commonest birds in England. However, today there has been a dramatic decline in their numbers. Between 1977 and 2000 sparrow populations fell by 65%. This has caused so much alarm that they have now been added to the Red Data List of bird species of conservation concern. There are probably many reasons for this decline, but it is certainly due to what we are doing to the environment and how we are managing it. Sparrow chicks are starving because of an insufficient supply of insects and spiders. In some areas, predation by cats might be another factor. The decline in the population of one of our most familiar birds is another warning (like the death of a canary in a coal mine) that we are seriously altering and poisoning our environment and must act.

This verse from the psalmist reminds us of the opportunity to help protect God's creation through our holy places. We can share our buildings and grounds with the rest of creation, and ensure that toxic sprays that kill the food of sparrows and other songbirds are not used.

40

'And why do you worry about clothing? Consider the lilies of the field, how they grow; they neither toil nor spin; yet I tell you, even Solomon in all his glory was not clothed like one of these. But if God so clothes the grass of the field, which is alive today and tomorrow is thrown into the oven, will he not much more clothe you – you of little faith?'

Matthew 6:28–30

It is unlikely that Jesus is referring here to a true lily, because the only one that grows in the Bible lands is rare and not particularly decorative. He is certainly speaking about an attractive flower that grows in abundance and decorates the fields of Palestine, a common plant known to the people. The one that best fits this description is the crown anemone (*Anemone coronaria*). This is a plant of open sunny areas, which flowers in the spring. It has beautiful royal-red petals and a black centre.

I like these verses because they clearly show that Jesus thought of wildflowers as creations of God which God especially cares for. In contrast we, God's stewards on earth, are not taking such good care of the flowers of the field. We have allowed many species to become extinct and many others are severely threatened.

These verses remind us that God's message comes to us not only through the scriptures, his book of words, but also through creation, his book of works. We need to sharpen our awareness to receive the message that nature is sending us. I am sure that it is not just telling us to relax and to admire the lilies of the field, but also warning us about the suffering that creation is enduring at present, and calling us to take action to protect it.

41

'Are not two sparrows sold for a penny? Yet not one of them will fall to the ground apart from your Father.'

Matthew 10:29

'Look at the birds of the air; they neither sow nor reap nor gather into barns, and yet your heavenly Father feeds them. Are you not of more value than they?'

Matthew 6:26

In St Matthew's Gospel Jesus introduces animals in his teachings on no less than twenty-seven occasions. Jesus was obviously very familiar with natural history, and the way in which he referred to animals leaves us in no doubt that he had closely observed their behaviour.

Here is a list of some of the animals that Jesus mentioned; they will remind you of his various parables and warnings: sparrows, locusts, dogs, pigs, wolves, sheep, foxes, doves, vipers, fish, camels, donkeys, hens, chicks, vultures, goats, a colt and, finally, a cockerel.

Today, within our urban life, it is tragic that so many people have no connection with or awareness of the natural world. And if one is not aware of an animal or plant species then there is no interest in conserving it.

I have spent my career working with various botanic gardens and am convinced of their mission within the cities of the world. They are rich green spaces full of plants and often birds and sometimes wild animals. All good gardens also have a children's education programme. This is one of the main purposes of the Eden Project in Cornwall.

I well remember taking a group of youngsters from Southall in London around the rainforest biome at Eden. At first it was too strange for them for much to sink in, but gradually they began to listen and learn. Things really sank home when I pointed out the rosy periwinkle (*Catharanthus roseus*) and explained that it is a miracle cure for childhood leukaemia. One of the group suddenly exclaimed that his young brother had leukaemia, and was now being treated with medicines that were probably from this plant.

As I watch the education staff of the Eden Project working with the many school groups who visit, I feel proud of the vital job we are doing in bringing children and adults into contact with God's green world.

'The kingdom of heaven is like a mustard seed that someone took and sowed in his field; it is the smallest of all the seeds; but when it has grown it is the greatest of shrubs and becomes a tree, so that the birds of the air come and make nests in its branches.'

Matthew 13:31–32

'If you had faith the size of a mustard seed, you could say to this mulberry tree, "Be uprooted and planted in the sea," and it would obey you.'

Luke 17:6

The writers of the Gospels were obviously struck by the illustration of the mustard seed as a symbol for the growth of the kingdom of heaven; it is recorded by all three writers of the Synoptic Gospels: Matthew (13:31–32), Mark (4:31–32) and Luke (13:19).

The Greek word used here is *sinapi*, and indeed the scientific name for one genus of wild mustard is *Sinapis*. The species *Sinapis juncea* does have a small seed that has the capacity for rapid germination. The exact plant referred to by Jesus is hard to determine though: mustard cultivated in fields rarely exceeds two metres and therefore is not a suitable place for birds to nest.

Rather than enter a debate about the exact identification of the plant in the Bible story, it is more important to listen to the lessons drawn from it. The idea here has been expressed in many ways. A well-known proverb is 'Great oaks from little acorns grow'. The point is the regenerative and growth capacity to be found in a little seed: a small work of God can become something large and significant. The capacity of the kingdom of heaven to break through and grow is a source of optimism that should still inspire us today.

After giving a lecture about the environment or the destruction of creation, I am often asked: 'Can the small things I do, such as turning off the light switches, *really* make any difference?' We should not be deflected from doing small things for the environment or for social justice, even though the crisis seems huge and insurmountable. If everyone in the UK switched off the standby lights on their electronic equipment there would be need for one less large power plant. Continue to recycle, turn off the lights and do any of the other small things for the environment as together they add up to a much larger effect.

'Listen! A sower went out to sow. And as he sowed, some seeds fell on the path, and the birds came and ate them up ... Other seeds fell among thorns, and the thorns grew up and choked them. Other seeds fell on good soil and brought forth grain, some a hundredfold, some sixty, some thirty.'

Matthew 13: 3–4,7, 8

The parable of the sower is one of many examples that show the familiarity that Jesus had with the countryside and nature.

The seeds of a crop need the right conditions to germinate, grow and yield a harvest. Likewise new believers need the right conditions and nurturing to become mature Christians. Some of the seed fell on the road, and the birds ate them up. These are people who hear the Gospel but ignore its message of salvation. Some seed fell amongst the thorns, and were choked, just as some believers are swamped by the many temptations of the world.

I think of the strangling fig of the Amazon rainforest. This begins when a bird excretes on the branches or in the fork of a tree, the excretion containing a seed from a fig the bird has eaten. The seed then germinates and the young plant begins to grow. Soon it clasps around the host tree and starts to put down roots towards the ground. Gradually the fig matures and becomes a tree itself, while slowly strangling, and eventually killing, the original tree. What begins in a small and seemingly harmless way can lead to disaster. This is what sin can do to those who do not keep close to God.

The parable of the sower calls us to continue to progress and grow in our faith rather than be deflected by the many distractions and temptations of life.

'Woe to you, scribes and Pharisees, hypocrites! For you tithe mint, dill and cumin, and have neglected the weightier matter of the law: justice and mercy and faith ... You blind guides! You strain out a gnat but swallow a camel! ... You snakes, you brood of vipers! How can you escape being sentenced to hell? ... Jerusalem, Jerusalem, the city that kills the prophets and stones those who are sent to it! How often have I desired to gather your children together as a hen gathers her brood under her wings, and you were not willing!'

Matthew 23: 23, 24, 33, 37

Jesus uses a variety of creatures here in his condemnation of the scribes and Pharisees, whom he finally calls serpents and a brood of vipers. This is one of several places in the Bible, including the Garden of Eden, where snakes get a bad press!

Plants are featured in these verses too. Mint, dill and cumin are all important flavours and useful plants. Here Jesus is pointing out their misuse in the practice of tithing. The scribes and Pharisees made their tithes publicly, in a conspicuous, boastful way: how easy it is to abuse the good things of life.

After using various metaphors from nature to condemn the scribes and Pharisees, God's love is portrayed by Jesus in a wonderful way through another observation of the nature around him. In my travels, I have often stopped and watched a mother hen gathering all her many chicks underneath her wings to protect them. The shelter and comfort of God's wings is readily available to anyone who seeks it. Many people today still reject this invitation of salvation but, through God's mercy, it remains open to all.

45

Jesus entered Jericho and was passing through it. A man was there named Zacchaeus; he was a chief tax collector and was rich. He was trying to see who Jesus was, but on account of the crowd he could not, because he was short in stature. So he ran ahead and climbed a sycamore tree to see him, because he was going to pass that way.

Luke 19:1–4

This is the well-known story about Zacchaeus, who was immortalised for climbing a tree to see Jesus. There has been a certain confusion about what species of tree Zacchaeus climbed because the King James Bible translated it as a sycamore. In the US the common sycamore, which is the plane tree in Britain, is *Platanus occidentalis*. A tree of the maple genus (*Acer pseudoplatanus*) is known as the sycamore in England. However, the tree that Zacchaeus climbed was in fact a fig tree (*Ficus sycomorus*), the sycamore fig. These trees can be up to thirty feet tall – so a sycamore fig would have given Zacchaeus a good vantage point.

As I reflect on this story, I think of the many trees I have climbed in the rainforest, either to collect specimens or to study their biology. One time I was working with a student studying the pollination of a *tauari* (*Couratari*) tree in Amazonia. We decided that we would work in two-hour shifts over a twenty-four hour period to see what insects and animals visited the flower. This involved climbing up the tree to about sixty feet above the forest floor. We performed this vigil, but were disappointed that nothing came to the flower. We did not give up though, and decided to repeat the experiment on another day. That day the timing of our changeovers was slightly different, and at dawn, at 5.30am, a large bee came by and visited the flower. We later established that this bee did this at exactly that same time each day. The first day this precise visit of the bee coincided with our changeover so we had missed it. Sometimes one needs the persistence of Zacchaeus to achieve one's goals, or to find Jesus in times of despair or difficulty.

The rainforest floor is dark, and in the days before GPS navigation systems, when you were hiking through the rainforest, it was hard to know exactly where you were! On several occasions we had to climb up to the top of a tree to see where we were going, and that is always hard work. Zacchaeus did not know where he was going in life when he climbed up into a sycamore fig tree, but the result was a life-changing personal encounter with Jesus. If you have not yet had such an encounter it is worth the effort. I have never regretted the day when as a student I made that pilgrimage to the front of a church to accept Jesus as my personal Saviour.

46

Then he sent out the dove from him, to see if the waters had subsided from the face of the ground; but the dove found no place to set its foot, and it returned to him to the ark, for the waters were still on the face of the whole earth. So he put out his hand and took it and brought it into the ark with him.

Genesis 8:8–9

When the time came for their purification according to the law of Moses, they brought him up to Jerusalem to present him to the Lord ... and they offered a sacrifice according to what is stated in the law of the Lord, 'a pair of turtledoves, or two young pigeons'.

Luke 2:22, 24

And John testified, 'I saw the Spirit descending from heaven like a dove, and it remained on him.'

John 1:32

Today many people keep doves in open dovecotes, to which they faithfully return. A neighbour of mine has a flock of carrier pigeons. Each day he releases these birds and they fly all around the town, circling in the air and happy to be free. Often they drink from the gutters of my house, but always go back to their owner. Noah used a dove to see whether the waters of the flood had subsided, for he knew that this faithful creature would return to the ark. The first time it returned with nothing there must have been great disappointment. But Noah trusted that God had a plan for him and released a dove a second time. Imagine the joy when the dove brought back an olive twig as a sign of hope for the future. Doves to me are a symbol of faithfulness.

Doves and pigeons eat the fruits and leaves of many different species of plants, and so it is quite logical for one to have brought a leafy twig back to the ark. These birds are important within the organisation of creation for their role in the dispersal of the seeds of plants. They ingest the seeds and may carry them long distances before they are excreted in another place.

The temple offering for Jesus was of two turtledoves, or two young pigeons, reflecting the humble home into which the Saviour of the world was born. It is easy to understand why he backed the causes of the poor and common people; and appropriate that later, when he was baptised by John, that the descent of the Spirit upon Jesus is likened to a dove.

I think of the various species of doves and pigeons that have become extinct due to the activities of humans. The dodo of Mauritius was a large flightless pigeon, and so had no means of escape from the sailors who visited the island and found them good to eat. It was not long before the last one found its way into the cooking pot. The tales of early settlers in North America mention the abundance of the passenger pigeon. Great flocks of these birds were to be seen. In spite of their abundance they did not stand a chance against the arms of the hunters. How often, through greed and ignorance, human beings have overused to extinction what could have been a sustainable resource.

And I say, 'O that I had wings like a dove! I would fly away and be at rest; truly, I would flee far away; I would lodge in the wilderness; I would hurry to find a shelter for myself from the raging wind and tempest.'

Psalm 55:6–8

Here is another text about a dove, which was made into a popular song.

Perhaps it would be nice to have the wings of a dove and to be able to see the world from above. However, the psalmist here seems to have wanted wings to flee from the bad things that were happening around him at the time. But fleeing is generally not the way to cope with our problems, as they will follow us around until they are resolved.

It is interesting that the psalmist uses the dove here because doves are notoriously sensitive to threats, and the moment they sense any danger will fly away. David did not fly away from his despair, for after recounting the many reasons for his troubles, he heads in the right direction, and in verse 16 of the psalm, he says: *'But I call upon God, and the Lord will save me'*; and in verse 22: *'Cast your burden on the Lord, and he will sustain you; he will never allow the righteous to be moved.'*

This psalm is a wonderful progression from complete and utter despair to confidence through faith and support from God. Perhaps it is just as well that we do not have the wings of a dove, but can resolve our difficulties down here on solid ground.

Jesus said to him, 'Truly I tell you, this very night, before the cock crows, you will deny me three times.'
Matthew 26:34

One of the slaves of the high priest, a relative of the man whose ear Peter had cut off, asked, 'Did I not see you in the garden with him?' Again Peter denied it, and at that moment the cock crowed.
John 18:26–27

To a Christian the familiar sound of a cock crowing is a reminder of Jesus' last night on earth. The Bible is made more believable by its recounting of the faults and failures of people, as well as their triumphs. It is encouraging to know that even Saint Peter had his bad moments. It is easy to deny one's faith or not stand up for it in a crowd of sceptics. And it is heartening that Peter is forgiven, and then trusted to lead the early church onwards. If we fail, we can take heart from Peter's recuperation, and the crowing of the cock can become for us a warning not to fail, and a reminder of God's forgiveness when we inevitably do.

I spend some time each year in a botanic garden on the island of Kauai in Hawaii. On Kauai many of the fowl that were brought to the islands by the earlier native colonisers have escaped and now run wild. Every morning before it is light – almost anywhere on Kauai – one is awoken by the crowing of these wild roosters, which echoes across the valley. I often lie in bed there and contemplate the symbolism of this sound. When we do slip up in life, it is important to repent and ask for forgiveness quickly before we fall into deeper trouble.

I think of the tiny spore of the fungus *Phytophthora ramorum*, which reached Cornwall hidden in a plant imported from America. This brought the Sudden Oak Death disease to the trees of the southwest when the spore germinated and infected its first tree. The disease has now spread to larch trees, and once infected, they die rapidly. This major pest began in a very small way but is now causing havoc to our forests as it spreads from tree to tree. To me this is a symbol of sin; a reminder to deal with our mistakes promptly before they swamp us and lead to destruction. We can depend on the forgiveness of God, and continue on the Christian pathway.

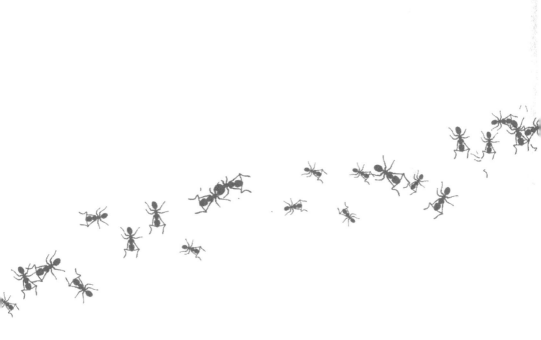

And in the case of an athlete, no one is crowned without competing according to the rules.
2 Timothy 2:5

Blessed is anyone who endures temptation. Such a one has stood the test and will receive the crown of life that the Lord has promised to those who love him.
James 1:12

These verses refer to the crown of laurel leaves (*Laurus nobilis*) which was placed on the head of a victorious athlete in ancient Greece, hence the use of laureate and baccalaureate in the English language today. This crown was made of fragrant young laurel (bay) leaves woven into a wreath. Few places use this way of recognition now, but when I received an honorary doctorate in Sweden a laurel wreath was placed on my head. I took this home as a memento and it hung in our kitchen for many months. Each time we needed a bay leaf to flavour a recipe it was readily available.

The laurel family is known for its many aromatic plants because each species has its own blend of essential oils. Cinnamon also belongs to the laurel family.

Paul and James used the laurel as a symbol of perseverance. Anyone who has participated in athletics knows that much training is needed to win. The Christian life is one that requires this perseverance and training – from Bible reading, prayer and worship – to keep us spiritually fit.

In the middle of its street, and on either side of the river, was the tree of life, bearing twelve kinds of fruit, yielding its fruit every month; and the leaves of the tree were for the healing of the nations.

Revelation 22:2 (NASB)

The Bible begins in a garden and ends with a vision of a city with a clear, unpolluted, tree-lined river flowing through it. The leaves of the tree of life are for the healing of the nations. This prophecy has meaning for us today. Did you know that more than 50% of prescription medicines originated from plants and trees? Many of these products come from their leaves and others from bark. About 50% of the poor of the world cannot afford prescription drugs and still depend on local folk medicine for cures, much of this from the leaves of plants.

I remember one time early in my explorations of the Amazon. I had very bad dysentery and the medicines in my medicine box were having absolutely no effect. We were staying in a shack belonging to a very simple and poor family. The good lady of the house made me a brew of orange and guava leaves, and I was soon on my feet again and back to the work of collecting and studying plants. The leaves of trees and plants are indeed God-given to us for healing.

However, there is a dark side to the use of plants in medicine. Many of the drugs we use originated and were developed from the knowledge of folk practitioners, without any benefits returning to them or their peoples or countries. The drugs vincristine and vinblastine, which are miracle cures for types of cancer, came from the rosy periwinkle of Madagascar, but that country has received no gains. This is just one example among many. Fortunately the world has woken up to this, and the Convention on Biological Diversity, which was drafted at the Earth Summit in Rio in 1992, obligates people and companies from signatory countries to return some of the gains from the exploitation of a plant to the country of origin. The intellectual property rights of the discoverers of knowledge are now better protected. Recompense from biodiversity was also the emphasis of the Conference of the Parties to the Convention on Biological Diversity held in Nagoya in 2010. The world is waking up to the rights of poorer countries and indigenous peoples.

This verse from Revelation is referring to a future time when presumably we will not be troubled by such abuse of knowledge, and when the leaves of the trees will truly be for the healing of all people.

CONCLUSION

At the beginning of John's Gospel we read that: *'All things came into being through Christ, and without him not one thing came into being'* (John 1:3). This puts biodiversity into its true perspective: all things came into being through the Word of God. God so loved his creation that he sent his Son to redeem not only people – but the entire creation or cosmos. Humanity is just one lowly part of the whole of creation. This link between Christ and creation means that following and living in Christ includes living in harmony with his creation. Christ's role in creation demands that we become its keepers and not its destroyers; the true Christian is someone who treats creation with reverence and respect. Creation is something that we are commanded to hold in trust as God's gift to us.

The words of John are echoed in Paul's words to the Colossian church, and seem a good way to help close this book of reflections on biodiversity: *'For in him all things in heaven and on earth were created, things visible and invisible, whether thrones or dominions or rulers or powers – all things have been created through him and for him'* (Colossians 1:16, NRSV).

The psalmist summed up the purpose of biodiversity – and much more – when he wrote: *'Let everything that breathes praise the Lord!'* (Psalm 150:6, NRSV).

'Praise the Lord from the earth, you sea monsters and all deeps, fire and hail, snow and frost, stormy wind fulfilling his command! Mountains and all hills, fruit trees and all cedars! Wild animals and all cattle, creeping things and flying birds! ... Let them praise the name of the Lord' (Psalm 148:7–10,13a, NRSV). One can't get much more comprehensive and inclusive about creation than this!

CREDITS

Page 10: Rainforest tree cut down © Ghillean T. Prance
Page 14: Deforestation © Ghillean T. Prance
Page 17: Pistachios © Olga Traskevych/123RF.com
Page 19: Aymara market © Ghillean T. Prance
Page 23: Yanomami at Toototobi © Ghillean T. Prance
Page 24: Rice sack © Valentin Oleynikov/123RF.com
Page 28: Lions © S.P. Crosby
Page 31: Ants on an avocado © Ghillean T. Prance
Page 33: Water hyacinths © Deborah Benbrook/123RF.com
Page 35: Donkey © Alex Postovski/123RF.com
Page 37: Caper plants © Paolo Amiotti/123RF.com
Page 41: Ostriches © Ghillean T. Prance
Page 47: Flooded rainforest © Ghillean T. Prance
Page 52: Date palm © Scott Riley
Page 59: Kapok tree © Ghillean T. Prance
Page 64: Saffron © George Tsartsianidis/123RF.com
Page 67: Rainforest clear-cut © Ghillean T. Prance
Page 70: Ewe and two lambs in the snow © David Coleman
Page 72: Cedar © Ghillean T. Prance
Page 83: Caterpillar © Ghillean T. Prance
Page 88: Rosy periwinkle © Ghillean T. Prance
Page 94: Sycamore fig © Ghillean T. Prance
Page 102: The author © Royal Botanic Gardens, Kew

Line and vector images created by Wild Goose Publications

INDEX OF SCRIPTURE READINGS

Nehemiah 2:18
Numbers 11:1, 2, 4, 5
Numbers 22:23, 32
Proverbs 6:6
Proverbs 13:22
Proverbs 14:31
Proverbs 30:18–19
Proverbs 30:25
Proverbs 30:26–28
Psalm 1:3–4
Psalm 55:6–8
Psalm 84:3
Psalm 92:12–15
Psalm 96:12b
Psalm 104:10–13, 16–17
Psalm 104:18
Psalm 104:20–22
Psalm 147:9
Psalm 148:7–10, 13a
Psalm 150:6
Revelation 22:2
Song of Solomon 2:1–2
Song of Solomon 4:13–14
Timothy 2:5

INDEX

INDEX OF SCIENTIFIC NAMES

SOME ORGANISATIONS INVOLVED IN CREATION CARE

A Rocha International
www.arocha.org

Christian Ecology Link
www.greenchristian.org.uk

Climate Stewards
www.climatestewards.net

Creation Care
www.creationcare.org

Ecocongregation
www.ecocongregation.org

Send a Cow
www.sendacow.org.uk

Tear Fund
www.tearfund.org

The John Ray Initiative
www.jri.org.uk

World Vision
www.worldvision.org.uk